ANNE GEDDES

My Baby Brother

Hodder Moa Beckett

ANNE GEDDES ™

ISBN 1-86958-651-4

© Anne Geddes 1997

First published in 1998 by Photogenique Publishers (a division of Hodder Moa Beckett)
Studio 3.16, Axis Building, 1 Cleveland Road, Parnell
Auckland, New Zealand

First New Zealand edition published in 1998

Designed by Frances Young
Produced by Kel Geddes
Colour separations by Image Centre

Printed through Midas Printing Limited, Hong Kong

The arrival of a new baby in the family is an exciting time for everyone.

Recording the events surrounding the birth and the progress of the new

baby gives siblings a chance to be involved in all the wonders of

watching their new baby brother or sister grow.

Contents

Our New Baby

His name is ....

His Birth

He was born on (date) .... at (time)

Day of the week .... His weight was .... He measured

He was born at .... and delivered by ....

The special thing about his birth was ....

Present at his birth were ....

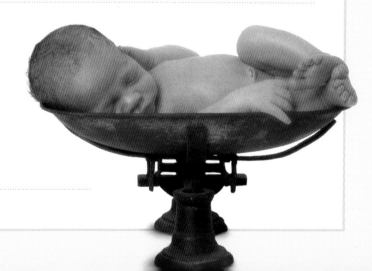

....

His hospital tag

His birth notice

His Birth Signs

His star sign is .... My sign is ....

He was born in the Chinese Year of the ....

His birth stone is .... His birth flower is ....

His birth day star sign newspaper clipping

First Encounters

I first saw my brother at .... He was ....

Our address is ....

The people who live in our house are ....

....

....

Photographs

His First Visitors

Special gifts given to my brother were

How He Looks

His hair colour is ....

His hair feels ....

His eye colour is ....

His face is ....

Other special things about the way he looks are ....

....

....

Lock of hair

His Prints

His footprints

My footprint

His handprints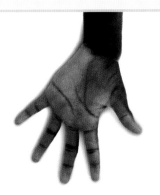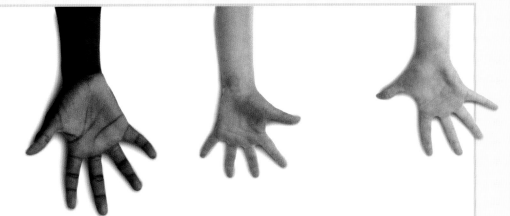

My handprint

Likenesses

.... *says he is like* ....

because ....

.... *says he is like* ....

because ....

I think he is like ....

because ....

Photographs

Naming Ceremony

Where held .... Date ....

Name of celebrant ....

Names chosen by ....

Meaning of first name ....

Reason for choice ....

Special clothing worn ....

Photographs

What people gave him

Who was there

Photographs

Our Family Tree

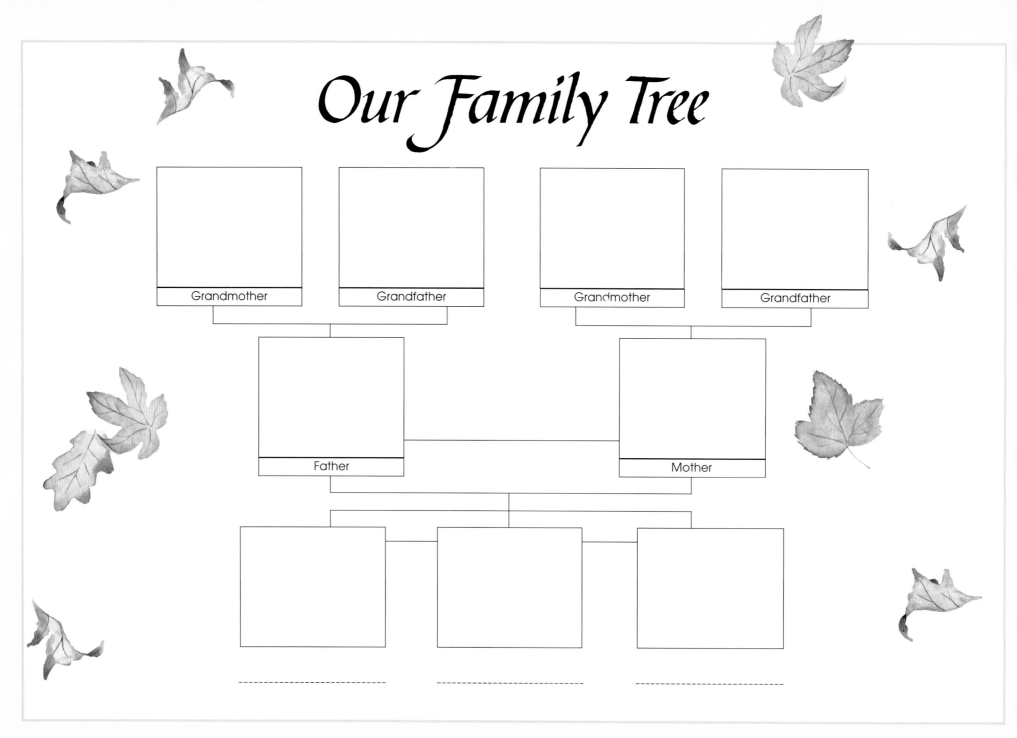

Grandmother   Grandfather   Grandmother   Grandfather

Father   Mother

Our Baby is Special

Special things about him ....

Our mother says ....

Our father says ....

I think ....

....

Special Names

Our family has special names for our new baby.

.... *calls him* ....

because ....

.... *calls him* ....

because ....

....

_____ *calls him* _____

because _____

I call him _____

because _____

Other names _____

_____

Watching Our Baby Grow

While he is very small he sleeps in ....

He rides in a ....

Bath time is fun because ....

....

We dress him in ....

He can ....

Photographs

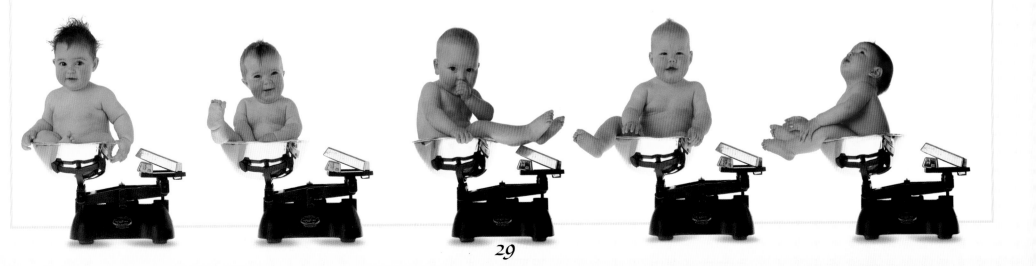

Now He is Three Months

Photographs

At Six Months

What he can do now is

What I especially like about him is ....

....

....

What I don't like is ....

....

Now He is One Year Old

What I think about my baby brother now is ....

....

....

....

....

....

Photographs

Good Times

Our family enjoys ....

Photographs

Favourite Toys

His favourite toys are ....

....

....

His best-loved toy is ....

My favourite toys are ....

....

Photographs

Favourite Music

Songs we sing to him ....

....

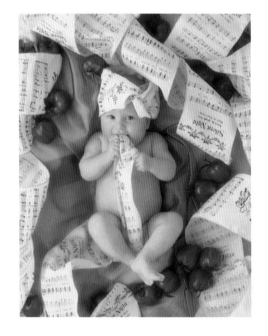

When he hears music, he ....

....

My favourite music is ....

....

Favourite Food

We feed him ....

His favourite food is ....

He won't eat ....

My favourite food is ....

I don't like ....

Favourite Friends

His best friend is ....

Other friends are ....

My best friend is ....

Photographs

Special Family Occasions

Our family always gets together for ....

....

....

....

My favourite holiday time is ....

....

Photographs

First Christmas

Where we spent it ....

Who was there ....

....

His favourite present ....

My favourite present ....

Special things about the day ....

....

The things I like best about Christmas ....

Photographs